AYN
RAND

SO THIS IS WHERE IT ALL STARTED.

She was born *Alisa Rosenbaum* in St. Petersburg, Russia on 2 February, 1905. *Communist* revolution was in the air.

Her Jewish parents had fought their way out of the *Pale of Settlement*.

Dad *Zinovy* had built a good pharmacy business. Mom *Anna* was the well-educated daughter of a prosperous businessman.

Education was the flavor of the day for Alisa and younger sisters *Natasha* and *Nora*; all had precocious talents, Alisa in particular in *literature*.

GERMANY DECLARES WAR!

Alisa's stable life came to a screaming halt during a family vacation in *Switzerland*.

The only way home was via *London* where Alisa conceived the idea of a career writing about heroic individuals who broke the envelope.

Alisa is enthused by her vision and her decision.

I'M GOING TO BECOME A *WRITER*.

Grade school was a huge disappointment to Alisa who thirsted for knowledge.

The family fled south to the **Crimea** with assets cleverly hidden from the **Communists**. Zinovy again built a pharmacy and Alisa attended high school.

PAPA, WHAT IS GOING ON?

THESE PEOPLE HAVE NO RESPECT FOR **PROPERTY RIGHTS**!

THESE BOLSHEVIKS WILL NOT LAST LONG. WE MUST GET BACK TO **PETROGRAD**.

They go back —all **five** of them— but to just one room in the house they once owned.

In high school, she discovered **Aristotle**, who joined other favorites such as Victor Hugo and later Nietzsche, Dostoevsky, Schiller and Edmond Rostand.

HOW **WRONG** COULD HE BE?

LOGIC

Zinovy and Anna found work, and Alisa went to university to study history and philosophy. She also discovered movies from the West and Viennese operettas.

MY PHILOSOPHY, IN ESSENCE, IS THE CONCEPT OF MAN AS A *HEROIC* BEING, WITH HIS OWN HAPPINESS AS THE MORAL PURPOSE OF HIS LIFE, WITH PRODUCTIVE ACHIEVEMENT AS HIS NOBLEST ACTIVITY, AND REASON AS HIS *ONLY* ABSOLUTE.

Her ideas jarred badly with her teachers and peers. They were totally horrified. Just in time, a letter from a cousin in Chicago who owned a movie theater arrived.

"She was never ever planning to return – and if she'd stayed, they'd have had her shot within a year!"

All family members enrolled in all kinds of squalid activities to prove their proletarian credentials.

Alisa sells some jewels given to her by her mother.

Following five weeks on trains, an ocean liner to New York City and another train to *Chicago*, she reached her relatives in late February of 1926 with $50 ($600 today) in her pocket.

Her intense, totally focused attitude and the noise of the typewriter soon exhausted the patience of her relatives who sent her off to Hollywood with $100 in her purse.

TO PROTECT MY FAMILY IN RUSSIA, I AM NOW AYN RAND.

"A hundred bucks then is, say, twelve hundred today. That is not ungenerous!"

She also has a letter of introduction to Cecil B. DeMille's production company from a local film distributor known to the cousin.

JUMP IN AND I'LL TAKE YOU OVER TO THE SET OF *THE KING OF KINGS.*

THANK YOU.

She joined the cast as an extra and met future husband Frank O'Connor. She married him in 1929 and became a US citizen in 1931.

I'M DOING THIS ONLY FOR THE MAN I REALLY LOVE.

In 1932, Universal Pictures bought her story, *Red Pawn*, which was never made, but the money allowed her to focus on finishing her first novel, *We the Living*.

The backgrounds of both the book and screenplay are clearly autobiographical and the plots are almost identical: young woman feigns love with Communist official to protect/seek release of man she really loves.

The dwindling money from *Red Pawn* allowed her to write her play *Night of January 16th*, a murder mystery, while she tried to sell *We The Living*.

"40% of jurors voted *guilty* but 60% voted *not guilty.*"

Night of January 16th had a modest run in Hollywood, and New York City beckoned. In late November of 1934 Ayn and Frank relocated; a 29 week Broadway run gave some financial independence.

While she voted for FDR over the simple issue of prohibition, she was becoming very angry about her fellow Americans' inability to grasp freedom.

I DON'T KNOW IF THIS WILL MAKE US MONEY OR NOT BUT IT IS A NOVEL THAT HAS GOT TO BE PUBLISHED.

We The Living came out in 1936 and was widely reviewed. Sales were slow but word of mouth kicked in and the print run was quickly exhausted.

THIS WILL NEVER SELL!

"Well, it hardly matters as she can now claim to have sold a movie script and a long run on Broadway and a novel sell out!"

We The Living was not to reappear in the USA until 1959.

Ayn began to plan her next novel, *The Fountainhead*. Published in 1943, it had by 2011 sold over 7 million copies and been translated into many languages. Today it still sells over 100,000 copies a year in USA alone.

THE FOUNTAINHEAD

a novel by

AYN RAND

I DON'T INTEND TO BUILD IN ORDER TO HAVE CLIENTS. I INTEND TO HAVE CLIENTS IN ORDER TO BUILD.

MY DEAR FELLOW, WHO WILL LET YOU?

THAT'S NOT THE POINT. THE *POINT* IS WHO WILL STOP ME?

Architect hero **Howard Roark** refuses to compromise his personal and artistic principles. He embodies personal integrity and independence while all around him people compromise and feed off others and the past using social approval as their standard of achievement.

HOLLYWOOD BLACKLIST

AMES CAGNEY

AYN RAND

LUCILLE BALL

TRUMBO

She obtained some work, based on her many languages, reading books for studios and she volunteered as a clerk for an architect to gain insights for her novel.

ANTHEM

a novel by

AYN RAND

author of

WE THE LIVING

Anthem was her shortest work of fiction by far. It is a futuristic dystopia novella in which man has entered a collectivist dark age. Individualism has been stamped out. American publishers rejected it but Cassell and Co in the UK brought it out to acclaim in 1938. It was not published in the US until 1946.

RUBBISH!

I *CHOSE* TO BE AN AMERICAN. WHAT DID YOU EVER DO, EXCEPT FOR HAVING BEEN *BORN*?

FDR OUT!

NEW DEAL = BAD DEAL!

VOTE WW for the REAL DEAL!

I CANNOT GO ON. THIS IS TOO MUCH.

Ayn volunteered to write bullet points refuting New Deal policies, but politics was not to become her beat, and she was already backing quickly away when FDR easily trounced Wendell Willkie.

YOU MUST PRESS AHEAD. THIS IS TOO IMPORTANT TO STOP NOW.

HE IS RIGHT, BUT THIS SURE IS *TOUGH*.

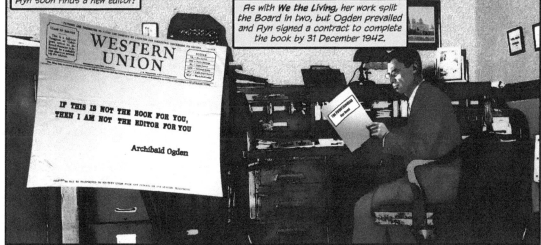

Ayn soon finds a new editor!

WESTERN UNION

IF THIS IS NOT THE BOOK FOR YOU, THEN I AM NOT THE EDITOR FOR YOU

Archibald Ogden

As with *We the Living*, her work split the Board in two, but Ogden prevailed and Ayn signed a contract to complete the book by 31 December 1942.

THE FOUNTAINHEAD
a novel by
AYN RAND
I AGREED TO DESIGN CORTLANDT FOR THE PURPOSE OF SEEING IT ERECTED AND I DESIGNED IT FOR NO OTHER REASON. THAT WAS THE PRICE I SET FOR MY WORK. I WAS NOT PAID.
IN A DEMOCRACY, ART BELONGS TO ALL THE PEOPLE.
HE'S JUST AN EGOMANIAC DEVOID OF ALL MORAL SENSE.
"As Howard Roark defends himself his arch enemy Ellsworth Toohey and his former friend, Peter Keating, listen to every word in court."
"The jury finds him not guilty."

"The Fascists have made *We The Living* into two movies thinking it is anti-Communist propaganda."

WHY ARE PEOPLE *FLOCKING* TO THESE MOVIES IN SUCH NUMBERS?

OH MY GOSH. IT'S JUST AS MUCH *ANTI-FASCIST* AS *ANTI-SOVIET*. WE MUST *BAN IT* AND BURN EVERY COPY IMMEDIATELY!

TEATRO

NOI VIVI / ADDIO, KIRA!

But one copy survived and Ayn helped in the long build up to its posthumous re-launch as *We the Living* in 1986.

Ayn and Frank relocated back to Hollywood, and while she was busy at the studios, he purchased a house with 13 acres, turning it into a commercial flower farm.

WHILE YOU WERE AT LUNCH WARNER BROS. CALLED REGARDING *THE FOUNTAINHEAD* AND WE ARE $50,000 *RICHER!* AND YOU GET TO WRITE THE SCRIPT.

"That would be well over half a million bucks today."

Sales of the *The Fountainhead* passed 100,000 and then 150,000, and she was on the best seller lists! But she was always homesick for New York City.

The making of the movie had been a nightmare for Ayn but she took some pleasure in seeing book sales immediately surge, thus returning her to the best seller lists.

AS AN EXPERT ON TOTALITARIAN PROPAGANDA, I AM *VERY* CONCERNED AT SOME OF THE CONTENT OF THE MOVIES COMING OUT OF HOLLYWOOD.

WHAT A BUNCH OF *LOSERS!*

She was not impressed by the caliber of committee members.

In 1951, Ayn decided to return to her much loved New York City to complete her next and last novel, which had the working title, *The Strike.*

Loyal Frank was sad to leave his 13-acre commercial flower farm but lovingly supported her.

YOU HAVE A DUTY TO WRITE A NON-FICTION TREATISE ON YOUR PHILOSOPHY, TO EXPLORE THE MORALITY OF RATIONAL *SELF-INTEREST.*

NONSENSE! I HAVE NO SUCH DUTY. BUT THE IDEA OF MINDS GOING ON STRIKE AGAINST ALTRUISTIC DUTY MIGHT MAKE A GOOD NOVEL.

AS SOON AS SHE HANGS UP I MUST TELL HER THAT THAT WOULD REALLY MAKE A *GOOD NOVEL!*

It would take 12 years to write all 1,146 pages, first six years part time in Southern California, then six years close to full time in New York City.

THIS CHAPTER HEADING, *ATLAS SHRUGGED,* WOULD MAKE A *MUCH* BETTER TITLE FOR THE BOOK.

I AGREE. IT *IS* MUCH BETTER. THANK YOU! YOU ARE *SUCH* A GREAT SUPPORT.

The climax of the book comes as railroad executive Dagny Taggart finally confronts the strike's originator, John Galt, in a high mountain valley where all those on strike live and work

The last six years of writing left Ayn burned-out, never to write another novel.

ATLAS SHRUGGED

Rand was savaged and both *author* and *publisher* were totally shocked and stunned.

RAND IS A COMMIE!

RAND IS THE DEVIL!!!

RAND IS A FASCIST!

HIRE AN ATTORNEY. THIS IS *TOO MUCH!*

NO. I'M SHOCKED AT THE ABYSMAL, STUPID, HOOLIGANISM OF IT ALL.

Initially, sales were poor, clearly damaged by these vicious attacks.

THIS IS JUST TERRIFIC. A REAL ANTIDOTE TO THE PAP WE HEAR EVERY DAY FROM THE ESTABLISHMENT. MAKES YOU FEEL A NEW SENSE OF PERSONAL CONFIDENCE.

THANKS, BUT KEEP YOUR COPY, BUDDY! IF IT'S *THAT* GOOD I WANT MY OWN COPY.

ATLAS SHRUGGED AYN RAND

Word spreads and two months later, *Atlas Shrugged* entered the top ten best sellers and stayed there for several months.

In 1962, she is the only female panelist on CBS's **The Great Challenge**, a program on America's future.

In 1964, she is interviewed in depth for **Playboy** magazine.

PLAYBOY INTERVIE

AYN RAND

MARCH 1964

A candid conversation with the fountainhead of "Objectivism"

In 1967, she appears on **The Tonight Show** starring **Johnny Carson** and was such a hit he invited her back twice more in five months.

"Surely a record or close to it!"

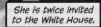

She is twice invited to the White House.

She is invited to address the cadets at **West Point**.

Ayn was now a major public intellectual with a growing audience. Young people in particular were attracted to her ideals.

For 25 years, she lectured, made public appearances and wrote about the ideas behind her novels while receiving many honors and accolades.

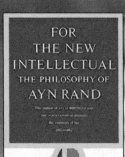

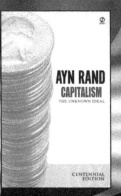

Her new career as a *philosopher* took off with seven books.

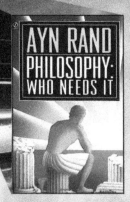

"Catholics and religious conservatives hated the atheism and egoism in Ayn Rand's philosophy. Liberals were offended by her glorification of laissez-faire capitalism. The middle-of-the-road was bewildered by her uncompromising tone."

Ayn has 3 plays, 4 novels, 6 movie scripts of which 3 produced and 7 non-fiction books to her name. And a new "Ism," a philosophy, *Objectivism*.

"IF YOU CAN KEEP YOUR HEAD WHEN ALL ABOUT YOU ARE LOSING THEIRS AND BLAMING IT ON YOU. IF YOU CAN TRUST YOURSELF WHEN ALL MEN DOUBT YOU..."*

FRANK O'CONNOR
1897
1979

AYN RAND O'CONNOR
1905
1982

*From Rudyard Kipling's "If".

Frank pre-deceased her in 1979, and she passed away in her New York City apartment 6 March 1982 working on adapting *Atlas Shrugged* into a TV mini series.

MICHELE BACHMANN

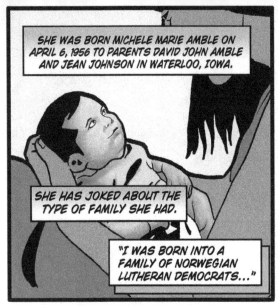

SHE WAS BORN MICHELE MARIE AMBLE ON APRIL 6, 1956 TO PARENTS DAVID JOHN AMBLE AND JEAN JOHNSON IN WATERLOO, IOWA.

SHE HAS JOKED ABOUT THE TYPE OF FAMILY SHE HAD.

"I WAS BORN INTO A FAMILY OF NORWEGIAN LUTHERAN DEMOCRATS..."

WHEN MICHELE WAS STILL VERY YOUNG, SHE AND HER PARENTS MOVED FROM IOWA INTO MINNESOTA.

BUT UNFORTUNATELY, THE MOVE WASN"T LONG FOR THE FAMILY...

AS HER PARENTS DIVORCED SOON AFTER.

HER FATHER DAVID MOVED TO CALIFORNIA.

THIS MOVE LEFT MICHELE TO BE RAISED BY HER MOTHER JEAN, WHO WORKED AT...

...THE LOCAL FIRST NATIONAL BANK IN THEIR HOME TOWN OF ANOKA IN MINNESOTA.

WHEN MICHELE WAS A TEENAGER, HER MOTHER REMARRIED.

CREATING A FAMILY THAT WOULD END UP WITH NINE KIDS!

AFTER GRADUATING FROM ANOKA HIGH SCHOOL AND GRADUATING FROM WINONA STATE UNIVERSITY IN WINONA, MINNESOTA...

...SHE MOVED ON TO LAW SCHOOL.

IN 1979, SHE BECAME ONE OF THE FIRST CLASS OF THE O.W. COBURN SCHOOL OF LAW AT ORAL ROBERTS UNIVERSITY.

IN 1986, SHE RECEIVED HER JD FROM ORAL ROBERTS UNIVERSITY, MAKING HER ONE OF THE FINAL GRADUATING CLASS OF THAT LAW SCHOOL AT ORAL ROBERTS.

AND BECAUSE SHE DIDN'T STOP THERE.

SHE RECEIVED HER LL.M DEGREE, FROM WILLIAM AND MARY SCHOOL OF LAW, IN TAX LAW.

AND BECAUSE SHE WAS SOMETHING OF A SUPERHERO, MICHELE DID ALL OF THIS WHILE JUGGLING BEING A MOTHER AND A WIFE.

FROM 1988 TO 1993, SHE USED HER KNOWLEDGE AND EXPERTISE OF THE LAW AS AN ATTORNEY FOR THE IRS...

UNFORTUNATELY, SOMETHING HAD TO GIVE FOR MICHELE.

AND SHE MADE THE CHOICE TO BECOME A FULL-TIME MOTHER, LEAVING THE IRS WHEN HER FOURTH CHILD WAS BORN.

SHE HAS BEEN MARRIED TO HER HUSBAND MARCUS BACHMANN SINCE THEY MET IN COLLEGE IN 1978.

SHE AND MARCUS HAVE 5 CHILDREN TOGETHER: LUCAS, HARRISON, ELISA, CAROLINE AND SOPHIA.

YOU'D THINK THAT WAS A BIG FAMILY, RIGHT?

BETWEEN THE YEARS OF 1992 AND 2000, SHE AND HER HUSBAND PROVIDED CARE FOR 23 FOSTER CHILDREN.

NOT ALL AT THE SAME TIME, BUT 23!

SHE AND HER HUSBAND PROVIDED FOSTER CARE FOR UP TO THREE GIRLS AT A TIME...

AND HAD STARTED DOING SO IN 1992 AS A SHORT-TERM CARE FOR GIRLS WITH EATING DISORDERS.

IT WAS AMAZING WORK THAT THEY WERE DOING, AND IT DEFINED THEIR HOME AS A TREATMENT HOME BECAUSE OF THIS.

BACHMANN GREW UP IN A VERY DEMOCRATIC FAMILY, BUT LIKE MOST YOUNG MEN AND WOMEN, SHE WOULD FORGE HER OWN BELIEFS ON POLITICS AND LIFE.

DURING COLLEGE, SHE AND MARCUS WATCHED A CHRISTIAN DOCUMENTARY CALLED HOW SHOULD WE THEN LIVE?

INSPIRING THEM TO JOIN THE PRO-LIFE MOVEMENT. THEY WOULD PRAY OUTSIDE OF ABORTION CLINICS AS PART OF A PRO-LIFE PROTEST...

AND THEY WOULD TAKE PART IN WHAT IS CALLED SIDEWALK COUNSELING, SOMETHING THAT HAS BEEN CRITICIZED AS INTIMIDATING.

NOT ALL PRO-LIFE SUPPORTERS SEEK TO INTIMIDATE AS SOME ONLY SEEK TO PERSUADE OTHERS TO RECONSIDER.

TWO ADDITIONAL THINGS HAPPENED TO HER TO CHANGE HER BELIEFS IN THE POLITICAL REALM. WHILE WORKING ON JIMMY CARTER'S CAMPAIGN...

SHE BECAME DISENCHANTED WITH HIS VIEWS ON PUBLIC POLICY, ABORTION, AND HIS ECONOMIC CHOICES AS WELL.

THE OTHER HAPPENED WHILE READING GORE VIDAL'S BOOK, BURR.

SHE FELT IT WAS A MOCKERY OF THE FOUNDING FATHERS AND SAID TO HERSELF...

I MUST BE A REPUBLICAN!

AND IN THE NEXT PRESIDENTIAL ELECTION, SHE PUT HER MONEY WHERE HER MOUTH WAS AND WORKED ON THE PRESIDENTIAL CAMPAIGN OF RONALD REAGAN.

AND VOTED FOR HIM AS WELL.

HE WAS ELECTED DURING THE CAMPAIGN OF 1980...

MAKE MY DAY!!
★ ELECT ME PRESIDENT ★

EAGAN
RESIDENT

GIVING HER A FIRST VICTORY OF SORTS IN THE POLITICAL REALM.

IN 1991, SHE GAINED ATTENTION IN THE MEDIA FOR HER ACTIVISM. SHE AND 30 OTHERS STAGED A PRO-LIFE...

PROTEST OF A BOARD MEETING IN RAMSEY COUNTY, MINNESOTA.

THE MEETING WAS FOR A $3 MILLION APPROPRIATION FOR A MORGUE TO BE BUILT FOR THE COUNTY AT ST. PAUL-RAMSEY MEDICAL CENTER.

HOLY BIBLE

SHE AND THE OTHER PRO-LIFE SUPPORTERS TOOK GREAT OFFENSE TO THIS...

AS THE HOSPITAL HAD BOTH PERFORMED ABORTIONS AND JANE HODGSON, AN ABORTION RIGHTS PIONEER, HAD WORKED THERE. BACHMANN AND THE OTHER PRO-LIFE PROTESTORS DIDN'T FEEL PUBLIC TAX MONEY SHOULD GO TO THE HOSPITAL. IN HER OWN WORDS...

I HAVE BEEN A LANDLORD OF AN ABORTION CLINIC, AND I DON'T LIKE THAT...

IN 1993, SHE AND SOME PARENTS FROM HER AREA WORKED TOGETHER TO CREATE THE K-12 NORTH HEIGHTS CHARTER SCHOOL IN STILLWATER.

SHE FELT STRONGLY ABOUT EDUCATION AND HOW IT WAS BEING PROVIDED TO STUDENTS...

BUT SHE HAD TO LEAVE THE BOARD FOR THE CHARTER SCHOOL SOON AFTER THEY STARTED.

PARENTS HAD BEGUN COMPLAINING OF HER CHRISTIAN TEACHINGS.

BUT IT WASN'T HER LAST FORAY INTO EDUCATION BY ANY MEANS.

SHE QUICKLY BECAME A PROTESTOR OF STATE-MANDATED EDUCATIONAL STANDARDS, SPEAKING OUT AGAINST THEM AND HOW THE STATES FOCUSED ON ONLY CERTAIN ASPECTS OF EDUCATION.

THIS WOULD BE ANOTHER STEPPING STONE FOR HER MOVE INTO POLITICS.

ONE OF THE BIGGEST THINGS SHE SPOKE OUT AGAINST WAS THE SCHOOL-TO-WORK POLICIES OF MINNESOTA. SHE FELT...

"SCHOOL-TO-WORK UTILIZES THE SCHOOL DAY TO PROMOTE CHILDREN'S ACQUISITION OF WORKPLACE SKILLS, VIEWING CHILDREN AS TRAINEES FOR INCREASED ECONOMIC PRODUCTIVITY."

IN 1999, SHE TOOK HER FIRST STEP TOWARD POLITICS, BECOMING A CANDIDATE FOR THE SCHOOL BOARD OF STILLWATER.

SHE WAS PART OF THE SLATE OF FIVE, FIVE REPUBLICAN CANDIDATES IN THE ELECTION...

AND ALL FIVE LOST.

SHE BECAME THE FIRST REPUBLICAN WOMAN TO BE ELECTED TO THE HOUSE...

FROM MINNESOTA, SERVING THE 6TH CONGRESSIONAL DISTRICT.

IN ONE OF HER FIRST VOTES IN THE HOUSE, SHE VOTED NO AGAINST AN OPPOSITION OF THE IRAQ WAR TROOP SURGE. SHE DIDN'T OUTRIGHT SUPPORT THE SURGE THOUGH.

INCREASED TROOP PRESENCE IS JUSTIFIABLE.

IF THAT MEASURE WOULD BRING A SWIFT CONCLUSION TO A DIFFICULT CONFLICT.

SHE TOOK PART IN A DELEGATION WHICH VISITED SUCH PLACES AS IRELAND AND IRAQ, TAKING HER BRIEFLY INTO THE GREEN ZONE TO MEET WITH US PERSONNEL.

SHE WAS ENCOURAGED BY THEIR WORK THERE.

SHE AND OTHER DELEGATES WERE IN PAKISTAN TO MEET WITH PRIME MINISTER AZIZ AT THE SAME TIME AS SIEGES TOOK PLACE IN ISLAMABAD.

THEY TRAVELED BY ARMORED VEHICLES WITH SECURITY AT ALL TIMES.

BUT, AGAIN, SHE FELT HER VOTE IN THE HOUSE WAS JUSTIFIED BY THE SECURITY TEAMS AROUND HER AND THE TERRORISM SHE HAD WITNESSED.

IN 2007, SHE VOTED AGAINST THE COLLEGE COST REDUCTION AND ACCESS ACT WHICH WOULD RAISE LOAN LIMITS AND LOWER INTEREST RATES...

AMONG OTHER THINGS, ALLOWING MORE STUDENTS TO ATTEND COLLEGE. THE BILL PASSED AND WAS SIGNED BY PRESIDENT BUSH, BUT SHE FELT...

IT FAILS STUDENTS AND TAXPAYERS WITH GIMMICKS...

...HIDDEN COSTS AND POORLY TARGETED AID.

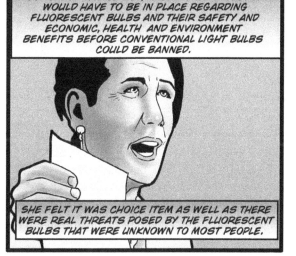

SHE INTRODUCED TO CONGRESS THE LIGHT BULB FREEDOM OF CHOICE ACT, ARGUING THAT A REPORT WOULD HAVE TO BE IN PLACE REGARDING FLUORESCENT BULBS AND THEIR SAFETY AND ECONOMIC, HEALTH AND ENVIRONMENT BENEFITS BEFORE CONVENTIONAL LIGHT BULBS COULD BE BANNED.

SHE FELT IT WAS CHOICE ITEM AS WELL AS THERE WERE REAL THREATS POSED BY THE FLUORESCENT BULBS THAT WERE UNKNOWN TO MOST PEOPLE.

ALASKA.

IN 2008, SHE BECAME AN ADVOCATE FOR INCREASED DOMESTIC OIL AND NATURAL GAS EXPLORATION IN THE ARCTIC NATIONAL WILDLIFE REFUGE AND THE OUTER CONTINENTAL SHELF.

SHE AND 10 OTHER HOUSE REPUBLICANS AND MEDIA MEMBERS TRAVELED TO ALASKA AND GOLDEN COLORADO.

TO LEARN FIRST HAND OF RENEWABLE ENERGY TECHNOLOGIES AND PROSPECTS OF INCREASED OIL AND GAS PRODUCTION IN ALASKA.

BACK TO THE U.S HOUSE FLOOR.

SHE IS SKEPTICAL OF GLOBAL WARMING, BELIEVING IT IS A HOAX.

CARBON DIOXIDE IS NATURAL, IT IS NOT HARMFUL.

WE'RE BEING TOLD WE HAVE TO REDUCE THIS NATURAL SUBSTANCE TO CREATE AN ARBITRARY REDUCTION IN SOMETHING THAT IS NATURALLY OCCURRING IN THE EARTH.

SHE OPPOSED THE WALL STREET BAILOUT BILL, VOTING AGAINST THAT AND FIGHTING TO BREAK UP FREDDIE MAC AND FANNIE MAE.

SHE ALSO CRITICIZED A BILL FROM THE BIG THREE AUTOMAKERS IN 2009 WHEN THEY ASKED FOR $15 BILLION, AS SHE FELT THEY WOULD ONLY ASK FOR MORE MONEY AFTER MAKING NO HEADWAY IN THEIR BAILOUT PLANS.

SHE HAD PREVIOUSLY FOUND HERSELF IN HOT WATER DURING THE PRESIDENTIAL ELECTION OF 2008 WHEN SHE STATED THAT PRESIDENT OBAMA HAD ASSOCIATED WITH SOMEONE WITH ANTI-AMERICAN VIEWS AND SHE QUESTIONED HIS VIEWS. IT LANDED HER IN HOT WATER WITH HER OWN PARTY BUT HER SUPPORTERS SIDED WITH HER.

ARDBALL

IN 2009, AFTER CHINA PROPOSED A GLOBAL RESERVECURRENCY, MICHELE BACHMANN INTRODUCED A RESOLUTION CALLING FOR AN AMENDMENT TO THE CONSTITUTION BARRING THE DOLLAR FROM GETTING REPLACED BY FOREIGN CURRENCY.

THAT SAME YEAR, DURING AN INTERVIEW RELATED TO THE CENSUS, SHE EXPRESSED THOUGHTS OF CONCERN RELATED TO THE PERSONAL INFORMATION BEING REQUESTED FROM THE CENSUS. SHE ALSO FELT THAT ACORN WAS TAKING PART IN THE COLLECTION OF THIS INFORMATION.

I KNOW FOR MY FAMILY THE ONLY QUESTION WE WILL BE ANSWERING IS HOW MANY PEOPLE ARE IN YOUR HOME.

WE WON'T BE ANSWERING ANY INFORMATION BEYOND THAT, BECAUSE THE CONSTITUTION DOESN'T REQUIRE ANY INFORMATION BEYOND THAT.

IN 2009, SHE MADE COMMENTS AND CONTRIBUTED TO THE DEATH PANEL CONTROVERSY, SPEAKING ON THE FLOOR OF THE HOUSE AS WELL AS SPEAKING AT EVENTS ABOUT IT. SHE STOOD AGAINST THE DEMOCRATIC HEALTH CARE OVERHAUL PROPOSALS, ASKING THOSE IN ATTENDANCE TO HELP MAKE SURE IT DOESN'T PASS.

SHE CONTINUED TO CRITICIZE OBAMA AND HIS ACTIONS, EVEN ON NATIONAL INTERVIEWS. SHE WAS ASKED ABOUT CUTS IN GOVERNMENT SPENDING AND WHICH ONES SHE WOULD MAKE TO REDUCE THE DEFICIT. SHE TALKED SPECIFICALLY ABOUT OBAMA'S TRIP TO ASIA AND HOW IT MIGHT COST $200 MILLION A DAY.

HE'S TAKING TWO THOUSAND PEOPLE WITH HIM. HE'LL BE RENTING OUT OVER 870 ROOMS IN INDIA.

AND THESE ARE 5-STAR HOTEL ROOMS AT THE TAJ MAHAL PALACE HOTEL. THIS IS THE KIND OF OVER-THE-TOP SPENDING.

A PENTAGON SPOKESMAN AND MEMBERS OF THE WHITE HOUSE RESPONDED TO THESE NOTIONS OF THE COST AND THE SUPPOSED SECURITY DETAIL...

...STATING THEY WERE INFLATED COSTS AND FIGURES AND THAT THOSE COSTS WERE IN LINE WITH PREVIOUS PRESIDENTS BUSH AND CLINTON WHEN THEY MADE SIMILAR TRIPS.

AFTER THE 2010 ELECTIONS, MICHELE ANNOUNCED HER INTENT TO SEEK THE HOUSE REPUBLICAN CONFERENCE CHAIR POSITION. SHE WAS SUPPORTED BY MANY REPUBLICANS AND THE TEA PARTY CAUCUS (WHICH SHE HAD FOUNDED).

BUT LOST THE POSITION TO JEB HENSARLING AS MANY OTHER REPUBLICANS WERE CONCERNED WITH HER FAUX PAS, HER TURNOVER RATE ON STAFF, AND WHETHER SHE WOULD ADVANCE HER POLICIES AND MESSAGES OR THE PARTY'S.

IT DIDN'T FAZE HER THOUGH. SHE WAS SELECTED BY JOHN BOEHNER ON THE HOUSE PERMANENT SELECT COMMITTEE ON INTELLIGENCE WHICH WOULD MAKE HER THE OVERSEER OF THE NSA, CIA, AND THE US INTELLIGENCE COMMUNITY. IT WAS A BIG STEP FOR HER AND FOR HER ASPIRATIONS FOR THE PRESIDENTIAL ELECTION.

SHE INTRODUCED LEGISLATION, AFTER BEING SWORN IN TO HER THIRD TERM, TO REPEAL THE DODD-FRANK REFORM. SHE FELT IT WAS DETRIMENTAL TO AMERICANS AND THAT IT KILLED JOBS. IT WASN'T MET WITH COMPLETE AGREEMENT BY ALL OF THE CONGRESS AS THERE WERE OTHER APPROACHES IN PLACE TO FIX AND REFORM THESE PLANS. MOST DIDN'T THINK IT HAD A CHANCE TO PASS.

SHE CONTINUED TO RUFFLE FEATHERS AS SHE GAVE HER OWN RESPONSE TO PRESIDENT OBAMA'S STATE OF THE UNION ADDRESS.

SHE DIDN'T INTEND FOR IT TO RUN COUNTER TO THE OFFICIAL REPUBLICAN RESPONSE, BUT KNEW THE RISKS OF IT SEEMING SO BEFORE SHE WENT IN.

TEA PARTY EXPRESS
REP. MICHELE BACHMANN'S RESPONSE TO OBAMA

SHE CONTINUED HER FIGHT AGAINST WHAT SHE CALLED OBAMACARE, CONTINUING TO CALL FOR ITS REPEAL. SHE CALLED ON THE HOUSE NOT TO PROVIDE FUNDS FOR THE ACT.

I'M VERY, VERY GRATEFUL FOR NOTHING ELSE, HAVING A MAJORITY IN THE HOUSE OF REPRESENTATIVES...

...SO THAT WE HAVE THE ABILITY OF THE POWER OF THE PURSE TO NOT FUND OBAMACARE, AND THIS IS EXACTLY THE RIGHT WAY TO GO.

SHE TOOK THAT MESSAGE TO THE PEOPLE, STATING THAT THE DEMOCRATS HID THE COSTS OF THE BILL AND TIMED ITS RELEASE TO AVOID THE HOUSE OR THE SENATE LEARNING OF THE COSTS, WHICH SHE STATED WERE $105 BILLION.

SHE CONTINUED TO SPEAK OUT AGAINST THE ACTIONS OF THE DEMOCRATS AND THE PRESIDENT SPECIFICALLY, NEVER STEPPING DOWN FROM STATEMENTS SHE HAD PREVIOUSLY MADE ABOUT HIM AND HIS VIEWS. BUT HER OWN COMMENTS WERE QUESTIONED AND CHALLENGED BY THE DEMOCRATS, SUGGESTING THAT THE BILL IN QUESTION HAD SHOWN ALL COSTS AND THAT THERE WERE LENGTHY DEBATES ABOUT EACH COST IN QUESTION ON THE BILL.

MEET PRESS   MEET CANDIDATE   DECIS

SHE SUPPORTS INTELLIGENT DESIGN AND ITS TEACHINGS IN PUBLIC SCHOOL SCIENCE CLASSES. SHE HAS EVEN GIVEN INTERVIEWS SUGGESTING THAT EVOLUTION IS ONLY A THEORY AND HAS NEVER BEEN COMPLETELY PROVEN.

SHE HAS ALSO CO-AUTHORED BILLS WHICH REQUIRED PUBLIC SCHOOLS TO PROVIDE ALTERNATIVE EXPLANATIONS OF THE ORIGINS OF LIFE. THE BILL WOULD REQUIRE THAT TO BE A PART OF THE CURRICULUM.

THERE ARE HUNDREDS AND HUNDREDS OF SCIENTISTS.

MANY OF THEM HOLDING NOBEL PRIZES, WHO BELIEVE IN INTELLIGENT DESIGN.

SHE HAD PREVIOUSLY OPPOSED MINIMUM WAGE INCREASES DURING HER TIME IN THE MINNESOTA SENATE...

...BUT NEVER BACKED DOWN FROM HER COMMENTS LATER. SHE BELIEVED THAT ELIMINATING FEDERAL MINIMUM WAGES WOULD WIPE OUT UNEMPLOYMENT.

SHE IS A STRONG ADVOCATE AGAINST NEW TAXES, IN ALMOST ALL FORMS. SHE HAD AT ONE POINT OPPOSED A STATE SURCHARGE ON THE COST OF CIGARETTES AS IT WAS A TAX, BUT REVERSED HER POSITION LATER ON THE ISSUE.

SHE IS A STRONG ADVOCATE FOR AMERICA. SHE DOESN'T BELIEVE THAT AMERICA SHOULD BE A PART OF THE INTERNATIONAL GLOBAL ECONOMY.

WE CAN'T NECESSARILY TRUST THE DECISIONS THAT ARE BEING MADE FINANCIALLY IN OTHER COUNTRIES.

I DON'T LIKE THE DECISIONS THAT ARE BEING MADE IN OUR OWN COUNTRY, BUT CERTAINLY I DON'T WANT TO TRUST THE VALUE OF MY CURRENCY AND MY FUTURE TO THAT OF LIKE A CHAVEZ DOWN IN VENEZUELA.

SHE SUPPORTS A FEDERAL AND STATE CONSTITUTIONAL AMENDMENT BANNING SAME-SEX MARRIAGE AND LEGAL EQUIVALENTS TO SAME-SEX MARRIAGE.

WE NEED TO HAVE PROFOUND COMPASSION FOR PEOPLE WHO ARE DEALING...

...WITH THE VERY REAL ISSUE OF SEXUAL DYSFUNCTION IN THEIR LIFE AND SEXUAL IDENTITY DISORDERS.

SHE HAS EVEN BEEN KEYNOTE SPEAKER AT FUNDRAISERS FOR THE CONTROVERSIAL CHRISTIAN YOUTH MINISTRY YOU CAN RUN BUT YOU CANNOT HIDE INTERNATIONAL.

SHE AND HER HUSBAND ALSO OWN A CHRISTIAN COUNSELING PRACTICE NAMED BACHMANN AND ASSOCIATES. IT IS PRIMARILY RUN BY HER HUSBAND WHO HAS A PHD FROM UNION GRADUATE SCHOOL IN CLINICAL PSYCHOLOGY.

THE CLINIC HAS ALSO BEEN MET WITH CRITICISM FOR BELIEFS THAT THEY PROVIDE CONVERSION THERAPY IN ORDER TO TRANSFORM HOMOSEXUALS INTO HETEROSEXUALS.

SHE AND HER HUSBAND HAVE ALSO RECENTLY INHERITED A PARTNERSHIP STAKE IN HER FATHER-IN-LAW'S FARMLAND FOLLOWING HIS DEATH AND THEY HAVE BEGUN RENTING IT TO NEIGHBOR FARMERS WHO WORK THE LAND.

SHE HAS GAINED SUPPORT FROM EVANGELICAL LEADERS, REPUBLICANS, AND NUMEROUS MEMBERS OF WHAT IS NOW THE TEA PARTY, A CAUCUS SHE HELPED BEGIN WITHIN THE HOUSE AS WELL.

SHE HAS BECOME ONE OF THE MAIN FIGUREHEADS OF THE TEA PARTY MOVEMENT, AND SHE HAS BEEN SEEN AS THEIR MOST VOCAL SUPPORTER.

THIS HAS HELPED HER IN HER MOST RECENT ELECTION IN 2010 AND SHE IS HOPING TO USE THEIR HELP IN HER BID FOR THE PRESIDENCY AS WELL.

SHE HAS GARNERED SUPPORT IN PLACES MOST POLITICIANS NEVER DREAMED THEY COULD, AND SHE BECOME A BEACON OF HOPE FOR MANY PEOPLE.

AND AFTER MONTHS OF SPECULATION, SHE ANNOUNCED HER INTENTION TO RUN FOR THE GOP NOMINATION FOR PRESIDENT OF THE UNITED STATES.

SHE PARTICIPATED IN A REPUBLICAN PRESIDENTIAL DEBATE IN JUNE 2011...

...WHICH IS WHERE SHE HAD ANNOUNCED HER FILING OF PAPERWORK.

BUT IT WASN'T UNTIL AN APPEARANCE IN WATERLOO, IOWA THAT SHE FORMALLY ANNOUNCED IT.

MICHELE BACHMANN

★ FOR PRESIDENT ★

NANCY REAGAN

THEY SAY BEHIND EVERY GREAT MAN IS A GREAT WOMAN

IT COULD EASILY BE ARGUED THAT 1ST LADY NANCY REAGAN STOOD BESIDE PRESIDENT REAGAN MORE SO THAN BEHIND HIM.

SHE WAS AFTER ALL A FEMALE FORCE TO BE RECKONED WITH IN HER OWN RIGHT.

NANCY REAGAN'S JOURNEY TO THE WHITE HOUSE WASN'T NECESSARILY A QUICK OR OBVIOUS ONE AS WE SHALL SOON SEE.

...T WOULD BE SOME TIME BEFORE NANCY WOULD ...SE HER PLATFORM AS A WAR ON DRUGS...

JUST SAY NO!

NANCY STANDING IN A SPOTLIGHT WEARING PRETTY RED DRESS.

ROSALYN CARTER PRECEDED NANCY REAGAN AS FIRST LADY OF THE INITED STATES.

NANCY REAGAN SERVED AS FIRST LADY OF THE UNITED STATES FROM JANUARY, 1981 THROUGH JANUARY 1989.

NANCY REAGAN WAS SUCCEEDED AS FIRST LADY OF THE UNITED STATES BY BARBRA BUSH.

FROM HER BEGINNING IN NEW YORK...

TO HER LIFE AS AN ACTRESS.

ALL LEADING UP TO PERHAPS THE MOST IMPORTANT ROLE OF HER CAREER. NANCY REAGAN IS MOST CERTAINLY A POWERFUL FEMALE FORCE.

NANCY REAGAN WAS BORN ANNE FRANCES ROBBINS JULY 6TH, 1921 IN NEW YORK CITY TO PARENTS KENNETH SEYMOUR RIBBINS AND EDITH LUCKETT.

NANCY'S PARENTS DIVORCED SOON AFTER SHE WAS BORN AND NANCY WAS MOSTLY RAISED BY AN AUNT AND UNCLE IN MARYLAND...

WHILE HER MOTHER PURSUED A CAREER IN ACTING.

NANCY DATED MANY HEAVY WEIGHT ACTORS AMIDST HER TIME AS AN ACTRESS. INCLUDING CLARK GABLE...

ROBERT STACK.

AND PETER LAWFORD.

NANCY WAS ACCIDENTALLY BLACK LISTED IN HOLLYWOOD BECAUSE OF A NAME COINCIDENCE.

LUCKILY, RONALD REGAN WAS PRESIDENT OF THE SCREEN ACTORS GUILD AT THE TIME AND CLEARED UP THE CONFUSION.

THE PAIR STARTED DATING SHORTLY THEREAFTER.

RON AND NANCY WERE THE BRAD PITT AND ANGELINA JOLIE OF THEIR DAY.

THE HOT PAIR GRACED MANY A GOSSIP COLUMN

AFTER A PAINFUL DIVORCE FROM FAMOUS ACTRESS JANE WYMAN, REAGAN WAS IN NO RUSH TO HEAD TO THE ALTAR AGAIN.

SADLY, THE RELATIONSHIP WITH HER CHILDREN WAS OFTEN TENSE...

ESPECIALLY WHEN THEY BOTH CHOSE TO AIR THE FAMILY'S LAUNDRY PUBLICLY IN TELL ALL BOOKS EVENTUALLY. MOSTLY DUE TO DISAGREEMENTS IN POLITICAL STANCE.

PATTI AND NANCY REUNITED AFTER RONALD'S ILLNESS TOOK A TURN FOR THE INEVITABLE WORSE.

THE TWO REMAIN CLOSE AND KEEP IN CONTACT REGULARLY AFTER THE LOSS OF RONALD REAGAN.

NANCY WOULD BECOME STEPMOTHER TO MICHAEL AND MAUREEN REAGAN, RONALD'S CHILDREN FROM HIS PREVIOUS MARRIAGE TO JANE WYMAN

NANCY WOULD HAVE AND MAINTAIN A CLOSE RELATIONSHIP TO MAUREEN OVER THE YEARS.

NANCY AND RON HAD A CLASSIC ROMANCE AND WERE VERY MUCH IN LOVE. OFTEN LAUDED FOR THEIR DEVOTION TO ONE ANOTHER.

CONSULTING AN ASTROLOGER ABOUT HER HUSBAND'S TACTICS?

STAR WARS?

REAGANOMICS?

RED SCARE? NUCLEAR WAR?

THE REAGAN ERA WOULD LACK NOTHING MEMORABLE AS A FOOTNOTE IN HISTORY.

NANCY WAS CREDITED WITH BRINGING A "KENNEDY-ESQUE" QUALITY BACK TO THE WHITE HOUSE.

NANCY LOVED THE COLOR RED CITING IT AS AN UPLIFTING COLOR. BRIGHT RED WAS EVEN DUBBED "REAGAN RED".

THEY SAY IMITATION IS THE SINCEREST FORM OF FLATTERY AND IF SATURDAY NIGHT LIVE IS LAMPOONING YOU, YOU'RE DOING SOMETHING RIGHT.

PHIL HARTMAN AND TERRY SWEENEY DID A HILARIOUS AND MEMORABLE RENDITION OF RON AND NANCY.

Just

A SCHOOL GIRL ASKED THE FIRST LADY WHAT TO DO IF ANYONE OFFERED DRUGS TO YOU. NANCY REAGAN'S FAMOUSLY HISTORICAL RESPONSE WOULD BE, "JUST SAY NO!"

Say

A RESPONSE QUICKLY PICKED UP AN REPEATED BY THE MEDIA, IT BECAME NANCY'S BATTLE CRY DURING HER TENURE AS FIRST LADY AND BEYOND WITH HER WORK DEVOTED TO DRUG ABUSE EDUCATION.

no

IN AN EFFORT TO SPREAD HER ANTI-DRUG AGENDA TO AS MANY PEOPLE AS POSSIBLE, NANCY MADE APPEARANCES ON POPULAR NIGHT TIME DRAMA DYNASTY.

WHAT 'CHU TALKIN' ABOUT FIRST LADY?

AND THE SITUATION COMEDY DIFF'RENT STROKES.

NANCY'S CAMPAIGN EVEN TRANSCENDED THE WORLD OF SUPER HEROES WHEN SHE ENDORSED AN ANTI-DRUG COMIC BOOK PRODUCED BY DC COMICS FEATURING THEIR MOST POPULAR SELLING CHARACTERS AT THE TIME THE TEEN TITANS.

THE FIRST LADY WAS LAMENTED FOR HER LAVISHNESS AND TASTE FOR EXPENSIVE THINGS WEARING A $10,000 GOWN DURING THE PRESIDENT'S INAUGURAL BALL WHILE THE COUNTRY WAS IN RECESSION.

AS ANYONE WOULD BE SUBJECT TO, NANCY'S REIGN AS FIRST LADY WAS NOT WITHOUT CONTROVERSY. HER PENCHANT FOR FASHION AND EXTRAVAGANCE EARNED HER THE NOT MEANT TO BE FLATTERING NICK NAME "QUEEN NANCY."

NANCY GOT THE LAST LAUGH AND WON OVER HER CRITICS BY DRESSING AS A BAG LADY AND SINGING "SECOND HAND CLOTHES" AT A BANQUET.

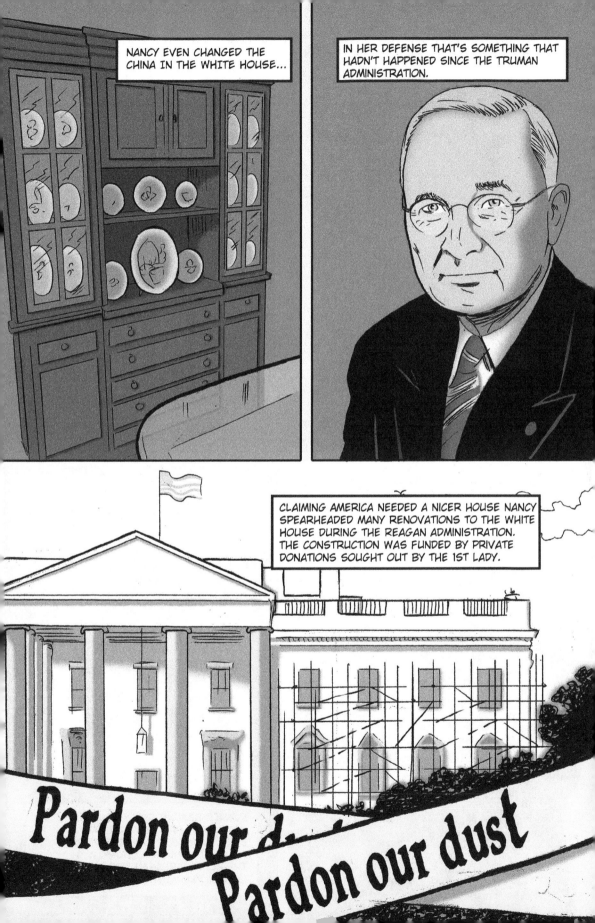

AMONGST AN ASSASSINATION ATTEMPT ON HER HUSBAND...

AND OTHER HISTORICAL MOMENTS- RON AND NANCY HAD A PRETTY GOOD RUN.

ALTHOUGH SHE STAYED ACTIVE AFTER REAGAN LEFT OFFICE, THE COUPLE RETIRED TO THEIR HOME IN BEL-AIR, CA. NANCY'S MOST ACTIVE ROLE WAS TAKING CARE OF HER AILING HUSBAND.

RONALD REAGAN SADLY LOST HIS BATTLE WITH ALZHEIMER'S HAVING BEEN DIAGNOSED 10 YEARS PRIOR. NANCY CONTINUES TO WORK WITH THE ROMALD REAGAN LIBRARY AND IS INVOLVED WITH STEM CELL RESEARCH.

LAURA
INGRAHAM

LAURA INGRAHAM IS ONE OF THE MOST RECOGNIZABLE AND SUCCESSFUL POLITICAL PUNDITS IN AMERICA.

HER NATIONALLY SYNDICATED TALK SHOW "THE LAURA INGRAHAM SHOW", WHICH AIRS THROUGHOUT THE UNITED STATES, IS RANKED EIGHTH AMONG MOST-LISTENED-TO RADIO PROGRAMS, WITH AN AVERAGE OF 5.5 MILLION WEEKLY LISTENERS.

SHE IS ALSO A POLITICAL COMMENTATOR FOR FOX NEWS CHANNEL AND HAS BEEN SO WELL-RECEIVED BY AUDIENCES THAT SHE IS NOW THE REGULAR GUEST-HOST ON "THE O'REILLY FACTOR".

HER WIT AND WISDOM HAS ALSO ENABLED HER TO BECOME A BEST-SELLING AUTHOR.

SHE IS YOUNGER THAN MOST OF THE MAJOR CONSER- VATIVE PERSONALITIES - AT 46, SHE IS MORE THAN A DECADE YOUNGER THAN RUSH LIMBAUGH, FOR EXAMPLE.- AND THE ONLY FEMALE AMONG THEM.

LAURA ALSO BRINGS A SNARKY BRAND OF AGGRESSIVE HUMOR FUSED WITH AN ATTACK-DOG SENSIBILITY THAT SHE EXPRESSES WITH A DISTINCT, CHALK-ON-GRAVEL VOICE.

SHE CAN ENGAGE IN SOBER, INTELLIGENT DISCUSSIONS WITH THE BEST OF THEM, BUT - WHEN PROVOKED - CAN RIP APART HER ENEMIES WITH INTELLI- GENCE AND GLEE UNMATCHED BY ANYONE NOT NAMED ANN COULTER.

SHE UNABASHEDLY WEARS HER CHRISTIANITY ON HER SLEEVE, WITH MANY OF HER OPPONENTS SAYING HER POLITICAL BELIEFS CONTRADICT IT.

SHE LAMENTS THE STATE OF AMERICAN CULTURE YET UNDOUBTEDLY HAS HAD AN EFFECT ON IT.

BUT THE MOMENT THAT IT BECAME CLEAR THAT LAURA AND HER 5 MILLION LISTENERS HAD REAL POLITICAL POWER CAME ON OCTOBER 3, 2005 WHEN THEN-PRESIDENT GEORGE W. BUSH ANNOUNCED THAT HARRIER MIERS WOULD BE HIS NOMINEE FOR A SUPREME COURT JUSTICE.

LAURA COULD NOT BELIEVE WHAT SHE HAD JUST HEARD. SHE HAD CLERKED FOR JUSTICE CLARENCE THOMAS ON THE SUPREME COURT AND CLERKED ON THE COURT OF APPEALS. SHE HAD BEEN IMMERSED IN LEGAL ISSUES MOST OF HER ADULT LIFE, ESPECIALLY AFTER LAW SCHOOL, STARTING WITH HER COURTSHIP BY AND WORKING FOR A LAW FIRM. .SHE HAD THOUGHT BUSH HAD A GOLDEN OPPORTUNITY TO TAKE BACK THE COURT FROM WHAT SHE FELT WERE JUDICIAL ACTIVISTS AND PEOPLE WHO HAD "CONSTITUTIONALIZED" THINGS LIKE ABORTION.

INSTEAD, BUSH HAD CHOSEN SOMEONE WHO HAD NEVER BEEN AT THE FOREFRONT OF CONSTITUTIONAL BATTLES, NEVER WRITTEN ABOUT THEM, DIDN'T KNOW ANYTHING ABOUT THEM AND WAS NOT KNOWN AS A JUDICIAL CONSERVATIVE ORIGINALIST BY ANYONE WHO STUDIES SUCH THINGS.

EVEN SOME OF LAURA'S LISTENERS WERE MAD AT HER FOR HER FIERCE OPPOSITION TO MIERS.

THE REACTION TO MIERS' NOMINATION EXEMPLIFIED HOW POTENT THE "NEW MEDIA" HAD BECOME IN THE LESS THAN TWO DECADES.

AS EVIDENCE, BUSH WITHDREW MIERS' NOMINATION AT HER REQUEST A MERE 24 DAYS AFTER HE CHOSE HER. THE POWER OF THE NEW MEDIA – LARGELY CONSERVATIVE – COULD NO LONGER BE IN DISPUTE.

LIVE
9:32 pm

MIERS NOMINATION
WITHDRAWN

PRETTY IMPRESSIVE FOR A WOMAN WHO BEGAN WORKING AS A CRIMINAL DEFENSE ATTORNEY TO WHITE-COLLAR CRIMINALS FOR SKADDEN, ARPS, SLATE, MEAGHER & FLOM AND WHO BURST ON THE SCENE AS ONE OF THE NEW "HIPUBLICANS" BY ESPOUSING CONSERVATIVE IDEALS IN A 1995 ISSUE OF THE NEW YORK TIMES MAGAZINE WHILE WEARING A LEOPARDSKIN MINISKIRT ON THE SAME ISSUE'S COVER.

A WOMAN WHO SEEMED TO BE INTENT ON SMASHING THE OLD STEREOTYPES OF CONSERVATIVE WOMEN AS WASP-Y COUNTRY-CLUB WIVES OR BIBLE-STUDY MOMS FROM THE MIDWEST TO SMITHEREENS.

FROM THE START, SHE SEEMED TO EPITOMIZE LADIES WHO WERE INCREASINGLY BEING CATEGORIZED AS "STILETTO CONSERVATIVES" – THAT IS, WOMEN WHO EXUDE SEXINESS BUT ALSO CLEARLY DON'T NEED THEIR HANDS HELD -.AND TO LEAD THE WAY FOR OTHER HOSTS AND LISTENERS.

INDEED, LAURA'S SHOW POSSESSES THE FIFTH LARGEST AUDIENCE AMONG TALK SHOWS BROADCASTING NATIONALLY. SHE ONLY TRAILS CONSERVATIVE GIANTS RUSH LIMBAUGH, LAURA SCHLESSINGER, MICHAEL SAVAGE AND SEAN HANNITY.

THAT'S A LOT OF INFLUENCE AND POWER, BUT TO REALLY UNDERSTAND LAURA INGRAHAM AND WHY SHE IS SUCH A PASSIONATE SOLDIER IN THE NATION'S CULTURAL WAR, WE NEED TO SEE A MOMENT WHEN SHE WAS AT HER MOST VULNERABLE....

IT WAS OCTOBER 2005 AND LAURA WAS RECOVERING FROM A CHEMOTHERAPY TREATMENT IN HER BATTLE AGAINST BREAST CANCER.

SUDDENLY, SHE HEARD A KNOCK ON HER DOOR.

BE RIGHT THERE!

LAURA WAS IN THE MIDDLE OF RADIATION TREATMENT DURING HER FOURTH ROUND OF CHEMOTHERAPY AND WAS PRETTY FRAIL.

SHE NORMALLY DIDN'T ANSWER HER DOOR NO MATTER WHO WAS THERE.

I HOPE THIS IS IMPORTANT!

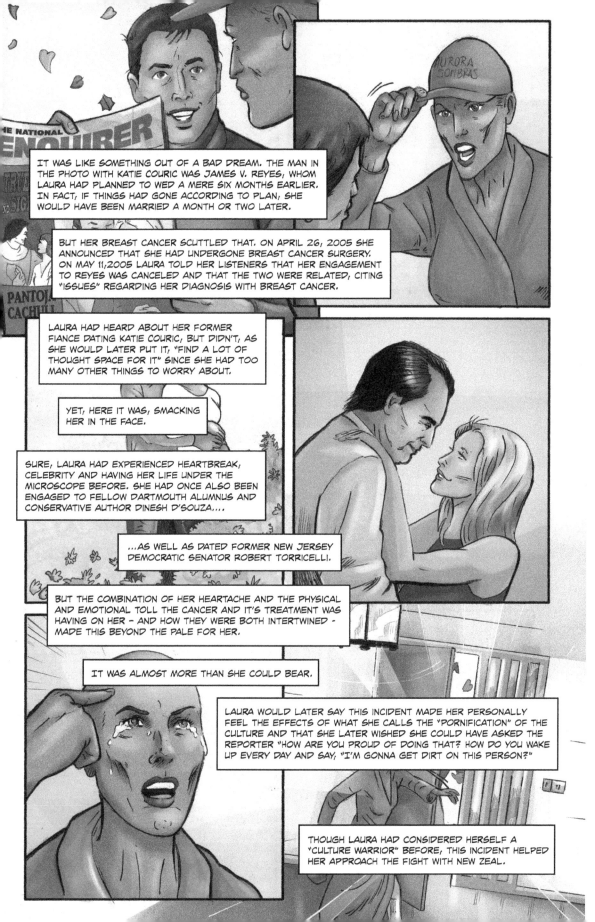

IT WAS LIKE SOMETHING OUT OF A BAD DREAM. THE MAN IN THE PHOTO WITH KATIE COURIC WAS JAMES V. REYES, WHOM LAURA HAD PLANNED TO WED A MERE SIX MONTHS EARLIER. IN FACT, IF THINGS HAD GONE ACCORDING TO PLAN, SHE WOULD HAVE BEEN MARRIED A MONTH OR TWO LATER.

BUT HER BREAST CANCER SCUTTLED THAT. ON APRIL 26, 2005 SHE ANNOUNCED THAT SHE HAD UNDERGONE BREAST CANCER SURGERY. ON MAY 11, 2005 LAURA TOLD HER LISTENERS THAT HER ENGAGEMENT TO REYES WAS CANCELED AND THAT THE TWO WERE RELATED; CITING "ISSUES" REGARDING HER DIAGNOSIS WITH BREAST CANCER.

LAURA HAD HEARD ABOUT HER FORMER FIANCE DATING KATIE COURIC, BUT DIDN'T, AS SHE WOULD LATER PUT IT, "FIND A LOT OF THOUGHT SPACE FOR IT" SINCE SHE HAD TOO MANY OTHER THINGS TO WORRY ABOUT.

YET, HERE IT WAS, SMACKING HER IN THE FACE.

SURE, LAURA HAD EXPERIENCED HEARTBREAK, CELEBRITY AND HAVING HER LIFE UNDER THE MICROSCOPE BEFORE. SHE HAD ONCE ALSO BEEN ENGAGED TO FELLOW DARTMOUTH ALUMNUS AND CONSERVATIVE AUTHOR DINESH D'SOUZA,....

...AS WELL AS DATED FORMER NEW JERSEY DEMOCRATIC SENATOR ROBERT TORRICELLI.

BUT THE COMBINATION OF HER HEARTACHE AND THE PHYSICAL AND EMOTIONAL TOLL THE CANCER AND IT'S TREATMENT WAS HAVING ON HER – AND HOW THEY WERE BOTH INTERTWINED - MADE THIS BEYOND THE PALE FOR HER.

IT WAS ALMOST MORE THAN SHE COULD BEAR.

LAURA WOULD LATER SAY THIS INCIDENT MADE HER PERSONALLY FEEL THE EFFECTS OF WHAT SHE CALLS THE "PORNIFICATION" OF THE CULTURE AND THAT SHE LATER WISHED SHE COULD HAVE ASKED THE REPORTER "HOW ARE YOU PROUD OF DOING THAT? HOW DO YOU WAKE UP EVERY DAY AND SAY; "I'M GONNA GET DIRT ON THIS PERSON?"

THOUGH LAURA HAD CONSIDERED HERSELF A "CULTURE WARRIOR" BEFORE; THIS INCIDENT HELPED HER APPROACH THE FIGHT WITH NEW ZEAL.

LAURA INGRAHAM WAS BORN ON JUNE 19, 1964.

INGRAHAM GREW UP IN MIDDLE-CLASS GLASTONBURY, CONNECTICUT.

THOUGH RELATIVELY WELL-OFF, LAURA'S MOM WORKED AS A MAID TO SUPPORT HER FAMILY.

LAURA GRADUATED FROM GLASTONBURY HIGH SCHOOL IN 1981.

DARTMOUTH

A VERY BRIGHT STUDENT, LAURA CHOSE TO ATTEND DARTMOUTH COLLEGE AFTER GRADUATION.

AS A DARTMOUTH UNDERGRADUATE, SHE WAS A STAFF MEMBER OF THE INDEPENDENT CONSERVATIVE NEWSPAPER, "THE DARTMOUTH REVIEW". IN HER SENIOR YEAR, SHE MADE HISTORY BY BECOMING THE NEWSPAPER'S FIRST FEMALE EDITOR-IN-CHIEF.

IT WAS NOT JUST WITH THE ISSUE OF HOMOSEXUALS ON CAMPUS THAT LAURA WOULD CAUSE CONTROVERSY WITH ONE OF HER STORIES.

HER TWO COLLEGE ROOMMATES, ANDREA AND DIANNE, FOUND THIS OUT FIRSTHAND ON AN EARLY SATURDAY MORNING IN JANUARY 1983.

SOUND ASLEEP AFTER A NIGHT OF PARTYING, THEY WERE AWAKENED AT 9AM BY A LOUD, REPEATED BANGING ON THEIR DORM ROOM DOOR.

STILL IN HER PAJAMAS, ANDREA OPENED THE DOOR A CRACK TO SEE A RECOGNIZABLE FIGURE, DARTMOUTH COLLEGE MUSIC PROFESSOR WILLIAM COLE. HE LOOKED ANGRY. THIS WAS NOT A GOOD THING.

DID YOU SEE THE ARTICLE SHE WROTE ABOUT ME IN THE REVIEW?

COLE WAS REFERRING TO LAURA'S LATEST COLUMN, TITLED "PROFESSOR COLE'S SONG AND DANCE ROUTINE", WHICH SHE HAD WRITTEN AFTER AUDITING ONE OF PROFESSOR COLE'S VERY POPULAR CLASSES CALLED "AMERICAN MUSIC IN AN ORAL TRADITION". THE COURSE WAS A NOTORIOUSLY KNOWN AS A "GUT" CLASS - MEANING YOU WERE PRETTY MUCH GUARANTEED AN "A" FOR SHOWING UP AND WRITING LEGIBLY ON YOUR FINAL EXAM.

BUT MORE INTERESTING TO LAURA WAS THAT, IN HER OPINION, COLE WAS USING HIS MUSIC CLASS TO PROMOTE HIS OWN MARXIST-SOCIALIST VIEWS ABOUT AMERICA.

HE ASKED STUDENTS WHAT THEY KNEW ABOUT POVERTY; RAILED AGAINST RACISM AND SEEMED TO BE THE EPITOME OF THE TYPICAL, UNHINGED "LEFTY" COMMONPLACE ON LIBERAL ARTS FACULTY DEPARTMENTS AT AMERICAN COLLEGES AND UNIVERSITIES.

LAURA, YOU'D BETTER COME BACK HERE. WE HAD AN UNEXPECTED VISITOR THIS MORNING.

NEEDLESS TO SAY, THAT MONDAY MORNING, LAURA NEVER SHOWED UP TO APOLOGIZE.

WHAT SHE DID DO WAS HAVE THE REVIEW SEND ANOTHER REPORTER TO "AUDIT" COLE'S NEXT CLASS.

PROFESSOR COLE THEN STARTED RANTING AND RAVING ABOUT LAURA.

THE REST OF THE CLASS WAS FILLED WITH COLE USING NUMEROUS VARIATIONS OF CRUDE ADJECTIVES TO DESCRIBE LAURA. THEN, BECAUSE SHE HADN'T COME TO APOLOGIZE, HE ANNOUNCED HE WAS CANCELING CLASS – INDEFINITELY!

THREE DAYS LATER THE REVIEW PUBLISHED A COVER STORY DETAILING PROFESSOR COLE'S PROFANITY-LADEN RANT. IT WAS A BLOCKBUSTER.

LAURA ALSO HAD THE REVIEW MAIL OUT A SPECIAL LETTER TO ALL 40,000 DARTMOUTH ALUMNI, INFORMING THEM OF THE SITUATION. THE SCHOOL BEGAN TO RECEIVE IRATE TELEPHONE CALLS FROM ALL ACROSS THE COUNTRY.

BUT HIS FELLOW PROFESSORS SUPPORTED BILL COLE ENTHUSIASTICALLY. AT THE NEXT DARTMOUTH FACULTY MEETING., PROFESSOR COLE RECEIVED A STANDING OVATION.

MONTHS LATER, PROFESSOR COLE SUED THE REVIEW, SOME OF IT'S OFFICERS, AND ME FOR $2.4 MILLION. SEVERAL YEARS LATER PROFESSOR COLE WOULD LEAVE CAMPUS AFTER ANOTHER CONTROVERSY.

THIS LITTLE DARTMOUTH DRAMA WAS MY OFFICIAL INTRODUCTION TO THE CONCEPT THAT DIDN'T YET HAVE A NAME – POLITICAL CORRECT-NESS. IT WAS A MINDSET THAT IN MY OPINION ESCHEWED EXCEL-LENCE, CRITICAL THINKING, AND ACCOUNTABILITY IN FAVOR OF FORCED SENSITIVITY AND RACIAL AND ETHNIC PANDERING

LAURA WOULD EARN HER BACHELOR'S DEGREE AT DARTMOUTH IN 1985, AND EVENTUALLY A LAW DEGREE FROM THE UNIVERSITY OF VIRGINIA SCHOOL OF LAW IN 1991.

BY THE LATE 1980S, LAURA WAS WORKING AS A SPEECHWRITER IN THE RONALD REAGAN ADMINISTRATION FOR THE DOMESTIC POLICY ADVISOR.

LAURA WOULD TAKE HEAT IN SOME QUARTERS FOR BEING ASSOCIATED WITH THE GROUP, WHOSE RANKS INCLUDE ANOTHER PROMINENT CONSERVATIVE, SUPREME COURT JUSTICE SAMUEL ALITO.

AROUND THIS TIME, SHE ALSO BRIEFLY SERVED AS EDITOR OF THE PROSPECT, THE MAGAZINE ISSUED BY THE CONCERNED ALUMNI OF PRINCETON.

LIKE LAURA, ALITO WOULD WORK FOR REAGAN. HE APPLIED FOR A JOB WITH THE "GIPPER'S" JUSTICE DEPARTMENT AND WOULD TOUT HIS INVOLVEMENT WITH THE CONCERNED ALUMNI OF PRINCETON WHILE DOING SO.

ALITO WOULD FIND THE ASSOCIATION MORE TROUBLESOME WHEN HE WAS NOMINATED TO THE SUPREME COURT BY GEORGE W. BUSH IN 2005.

AS LAURA KNEW ALL TOO WELL, MANY LIBERALS ACCUSED THE GROUP OF HAVING OPPOSED WOMEN AND MINORITIES ON PRINCETON'S CAMPUS, VICIOUS BIGOTRY AGAINST HOMOSEXUALS AND IT'S ALLEGED DEFENSE OF THE INTERESTS OF AFFLUENT MALE ALUMNI AND THEIR SONS.

HAVING ENDURED SIMILAR HARSH CHARGES HERSELF, LAURA DENOUNCED THEM ON AIR AND BECAME ONE OF JUSTICE ALITO'S MOST VOCAL SUPPORTERS – IRONIC SINCE SHE HAD PLAYED SUCH A CRUCIAL ROLE IN NIXING MIERS, THE FIRST PERSON PRESIDENT BUSH NOMINATED FOR THE SEAT..

HAVING ENDURED SIMILAR HARSH CHARGES HERSELF, LAURA DENOUNCED THEM ON AIR AND BECAME ONE OF JUSTICE ALITO'S MOST VOCAL SUPPORTERS - IRONIC SINCE SHE HAD PLAYED SUCH A CRUCIAL ROLE IN NIXING MIERS, THE FIRST PERSON PRESIDENT BUSH NOMINATED FOR THE SEAT..

SHE ALSO WOULD WORK AS AN ATTORNEY AT THE NEW YORK-BASED LAW FIRM SKADDEN, ARPS, SLATE, MEAGHER & FLOM.

LAURA'S MOST SIGNIFICANT AND HIGH-PROFILE JOB DURING THIS PERIOD WAS WORKING AS A CLERK FOR U.S. SUPREME COURT JUSTICE CLARENCE THOMAS.

AROUND THE TIME OF THOMAS' SUPREME COURT APPOINTMENT, SHE JOINED WITH A CONSERVATIVE GROUP CALLED INDEPENDENT WOMEN'S FORUM THAT FORMED A COMMITTEE TO ATTACK AND DISCREDIT ANITA HILL'S SEXUAL HARASSMENT TESTIMONY AGAINST THOMAS DURING HIS CONFIRMATION HEARINGS.

INDEPENDENT WOMEN'S FORUM'S OTHER ACTIVITIES INCLUDED TESTIFYING IN CONGRESS FOR DEFUNDING THE VIOLENCE AGAINST WOMEN ACT AND AGAINST AFFIRMATIVE ACTION.

LAURA ALSO CO-HOSTED A THREE-PART PBS SPECIAL ON "THE GENDER WARS," WHICH EXPLORED "WHETHER THE ADVANCEMENT OF WOMEN IN VIRTUALLY ALL AREAS OF SOCIETY CAN BE ACHIEVED WITHOUT A RETREAT, IN SOME WAY, ON THE PART OF MEN.". SHE ALSO LED A BOYCOTT AGAINST THE RAPPER AKON, WHO MANY VIEWED AS MISOGYNISTIC.

A CONVERT TO ROMAN CATHOLICISM, ONE OF LAURA'S MOST PASSIONATE POSITIONS IS THAT LIFE IS SACRED; ABORTION IS EVIL AND ROE V. WADE MUST BE OVERTURNED.

THE 1990S WOULD FIND LAURA EXTREMELY BUSY PROFESSIONALLY. AFTER HER NOW-LEGENDARY NEW YORK TIMES MAGAZINE COVER SHOT, SHE THEN BECAME BOTH A REGULAR MSNBC PUNDIT AND A COMMENTATOR ON THE "CBS EVENING NEWS."

IT WAS AT CBS WHERE SHE ASKED ISRAELI PRIME MINISTER SHIMON PERES A MEMORABLE QUESTION.

SHOULD THE UNITED STATES BOMB LIBYA OR SYRIA IN RETALIATION FOR THE TWA FLIGHT EXPLOSION?

THIS ANGERED AND DISTURBED MANY, ESPECIALLY ON THE LEFT SIDE OF THE POLITICAL SPECTRUM, WHO FELT THE CAUSE FOR THE EXPLOSION WAS UNKNOWN AND THEREFORE THE QUESTION BORDERED ON HORRIBLY IRRESPONSIBLE OR AT LEAST INCREDIBLY PREMATURE.

IT WAS CLEAR IMMEDIATELY THAT LAURA ARGUED POLITICS THE WAY LAWYERS ARGUE CASES (AND STILL DOES).

NOW, HOLD ON A MINUTE! THAT ARGUMENT SOUNDS GOOD, BUT THE FACTS SIMPLY DON'T BACK IT UP!

SHE IS A CLASS-A SCHMOOZER WHO UNDERSTANDS AND EXPLOITS HER VERBAL GIFTS TO THE FULLEST. SHE ALSO HAS A SKILL FOR NETWORKING.

HER LINGUISTIC GIFTS, SENSE OF HUMOR AND WILLINGNESS TO GO FOR HER OPPONENTS' POLITICAL JUGULAR HAVE ALLOWED LAURA TO BREAK INTO THE BOYS' CLUB OF CONSERVATIVE RADIO.

IT FORTUNATE THAT LAURA FELT A TALK-RADIO CAREER CALLING HER, SINCE HER TV CAREER HAD HIT A BIG DITCH. IN THE LATE 1990S, SHE BRIEFLY HOSTED HER OWN MSNBC CABLE TELEVISION SHOW, "WATCH IT!" (17 MONTHS AND THREE TIME SLOTS LATER, LAURA, DISPLAYING HER TRADEMARK HUMOR, JOKED THAT IT SHOULD HAVE BEEN CALLED "WATCH IT GET CANCELED!"),

AS THE DECADE DREW TO A CLOSE AND THE NEW MILLENNIUM APPROACHED, LAURA'S TV CAREER WAS SEEMINGLY STAGNANT AND HER TALK-RADIO CAREER HAD NOT YET BEGUN.

THEN A DOCTOR MADE AN ANNOUNCEMENT THAT WOULD CHANGER HER LIFE FOREVER.

I'M AFRAID YOUR MOM HAS LUNG CANCER.

LAURA'S MOM BECAME SO SICK AND FRAIL, LAURA WOULD HELP HER INTO BED EVERY NIGHT.

THE ROUNDS OF CHEMOTHERAPY HAD WASTED HER FIVE-FOOT FRAME TO SKIN AND BONES AND SHE NEEDED HER PILLOWS ARRANGED "JUST SO" IN ORDER TO SLEEP MORE THAN AN HOUR OR TWO.

THEN FOR SOME REASON – AND TO THIS DAY LAURA SAYS SHE STILL DOES NOT FULLY UNDERSTAND WHY – SHE FELT COMPELLED TO OPEN UP A BIBLE THEY HAD IN THE HOUSE ONE NIGHT AND START READING FROM THE NEW TESTAMENT.

IN THE FOG AND SADNESS OF THE NIGHT, LAURA DOESN'T REMEMBER THE PASSAGES SHE READ, BUT FELT THEY WERE SPEAKING TO HER MOTHER AS SHE WAS DRIFTING AWAY FROM HER.

DURING THE LONG DAYS AND NIGHTS OF HER MOTHER'S ILLNESS, MANY OF LAURA'S FRIENDS CALLED. THEY SAID THEY WERE PRAYING FOR HER OR ASKED TO PRAY WITH HER ON THE TELEPHONE.

BACK THEN, PRAYING WAS NOT SOMETHING LAURA NORMALLY DID AND SHE FOUND THE REQUESTS A BIT ODD – BUT SHE GLADLY WELCOMED ANY AND ALL PRAYERS..

LAURA'S MOM DIED IN MAY 1999, WITH HER ENTIRE FAMILY SURROUNDING HER.

LAURA HAD WATCHED HER TOUGH, FUNNY, HARD-WORKING MOTHER FIGHT UNTIL THE VERY END.

DESPITE BEING HEARTBROKEN, IT WAS UP TO LAURA TO FILL OUT THE FORMS FOR HER MOTHER'S BURIAL. IT WOULD BE UP TO HER AND NOT HER BROTHER JIMMY OR ANYONE ELSE TO CHOOSE HER BURIAL CLOTHES, WRITE HER OBITUARY; CHOOSE A CASKET AND RESERVE THE LIMOUSINE THAT WOULD CARRY HER MOTHER TO THE CEMETERY.

IT ALL GOT DONE, BUT LAURA FELT ALONE AND BROKEN.

LAURA WOULD TRY TO FILL THE VOID SHE FELT BY HER MOTHER'S PASSING WITH THINGS THAT MADE HER EVEN MORE UNHAPPY.

THOUGH SHE WAS HOSTING HER SHOW ON MSNBC, SHE WAS NOT REALLY ENJOYING IT. SHE WAS MAKING ONE BAD DECISION AFTER ANOTHER. IT WAS A MISERABLE TIME.

ABOUT THREE MONTHS AFTER HER MOTHER'S DEATH, LAURA REALIZED SHE HADN'T CRIED SINCE HER FUNERAL.

THIS SENSE OF DETACHMENT WAS NOT "NORMAL".

FOR A TIME, LAURA BURIED HERSELF IN HER WORK AND GIVING SPEECHES IN A FUTILE ATTEMPT TO DO AN END-RUN AROUND HER GRIEF - WHICH ONLY MADE MATTERS WORSE.

IT WOULD TAKE LAURA YEARS BEFORE SHE FINALLY LET HERSELF REMEMBER HER MOTHER - AND APPRECIATE ALL SHE HAD GIVEN HER.

FOR A LONG TIME, IT HAD SIMPLY BEEN TOO PAINFUL FOR HER TO RECALL WHAT SHE HAD DONE FOR LAURA AND LAURA'S BROTHERS. - HOW SHE DID WITHOUT SO THEY COULD HAVE NICE CLOTHES OR A USED CAR.

LAURA RECALLED HOW HER MOM WORKED AT WILLIE'S STEAKHOUSE INTO HER 70S "UNTIL THEY LET ALL THE OLD GALS GO" SO SHE COULD PAY FOR HER KIDS' TUITION.

IN THE AFTERMATH OF HER MOM'S PASSING, LAURA GRADUALLY BEGAN TO SENSE GOD'S PRESENCE IN HER LIFE. SHE NOW CONSIDERS THIS HER MOTHER'S FINAL GIFT TO HER.

IN THE AFTERMATH OF HER MOM'S PASSING, LAURA GRADUALLY BEGAN TO SENSE GOD'S PRESENCE IN HER LIFE. SHE NOW CONSIDERS THIS HER MOTHER'S FINAL GIFT TO HER.

THEY HAD ATTENDED THE PILGRIM BAPTIST CHURCH IN GLASTONBURY, CONNECTICUT., A CONSERVATIVE FAMILY CHURCH FILLED WITH CHEERFUL, OUTGOING PEOPLE.

LAURA WENT TO SUMMER SCHOOL AND HATED IT.

SHE ENJOYED THE FOOD, SPORTS AND GAMES AT THE CHURCH'S PICNICS.

SHE ALSO WENT TO SUMMER BIBLE CAMP AND HATED IT.

LAURA REMEMBERS THE CHURCH'S PASTOR, HOWARD WOOD, SHAKING HER HAND EVERY WEEK WITH A BIG SMILE ON HIS FACE.

THE PASTOR'S WORDS ALWAYS MADE LAURA FEEL EXTREMELY HAPPY, LIKE SHE WAS TEN FEET TALL

LAURA'S DAD STOPPED GOING TO CHURCH FIRST AND THEN HER MOTHER – WHO HAD BEEN RAISED CATHOLIC- STOPPED AS WELL. SHE NEVER KNEW THE REASON WHY AND NEVER ASKED.

SHE JUST REMEMBERED SAYING A BEDTIME PRAYER EVERY NIGHT BEFORE GOING TO SLEEP.

IN SHORT, GOD WAS SUDDENLY NOT A BIG TOPIC OF CONVERSATION IN LAURA'S HIME;WHICH IS WHAT HAS MADE LAURA'S RELATIVELY RECENT CONVERSION TO THE CATHOLIC FAITH ALL THE MORE REMARKABLE.

SHE TELLS FRIENDS JOKINGLY; "I'M HALF-POLISH, SO IT WAS A JOHN PAUL II THING!"

HOWEVER, SHE TRUTHFULLY FEELS THE HOLY SPIRIT CAME TO HER.

LAURA HAD STILL NOT DEALT WITH HER MOTHER'S DEATH WHEN SHE WENT TO SEE AN OLD FRIEND OF HERS, PASTOR PAT CIPOLLONE, FOR LUNCH.

SO HOW ARE YOU DOING, LAURA?

I'M JUST REALLY UNHAPPY. I DON'T KNOW WHAT'S HAPPENING TO ME. WHAT MY LIFE HAS BECOME.

IT WAS THEN THAT MONTHS OF LAURA'S PENT-UP EMOTION AND TEARS CAME FLOWING.

IT'S GONNA BE FINE..

THOUGH ANGRY AT THE TIME, LAURA NOW FEELS THAT GOD WAS USING HER FRIEND TO REACH OUT TO HER AND WAS TRYING TO GET HER ATTENTION.

I DON'T NEED THIS, OKAY? I DON'T NEED TO GO AND DO THIS!

LAURA WOULD ULTIMATELY GO SEE A PRIEST IN WASHINGTON, MONSIGNOR PETER VAGHI.

LAURA WAS AMAZED. HERE WAS SOMEONE SHE ALREADY HAD SOMETHING IN COMMON WITH! HE BECAME A PRIEST AFTER BEING A LAWYER, MUCH AS SHE WAS A LAWYER AND HAD MOVED ONTO SOMETHING ELSE.

MONSIGNOR VAGHI WOULD HELP GUIDE LAURA TO A PLACE SHE NEVER THOUGHT SHE WOULD BE. EVEN TODAY, IT'S HARD FOR HER TO TALK ABOUT WHAT HAPPENED, BECAUSE IT'S HARD FOR EVEN HER TO REALIZE WHAT EXACTLY HAPPENED.

LAURA WOULD READ A BIT TO HELP HER COPE WITH HOW SHE WAS TRANSFORMING INSIDE AND WHY.

THE BEST EXPLANATION SHE COULD COME UP WITH WAS THAT GOD WAS WORKING THROUGH PEOPLE LIKE PASTOR CIPOLLONE AND MONSIGNOR VAGHI AND HER CLOSE FRIENDS TO REACH HER.

AT EASTER VIGIL IN 2003, LAURA WAS BAPTIZED BY MONSIGNOR VAGHI, WAS CONFIRMED AND RECEIVED HER FIRST HOLY COMMUNION. SHE CHOSE CARO-LINE, HER MOTHER'S MIDDLE NAME AS HER COMMUNION NAME.

LAURA'S NEWFOUND FAITH WAS LIKE A ROCK FOR HER DURING HER BATTLE WITH CANCER IN 2005.

LAURA WAS TALKING WITH PASTOR PAT CIPOLLONE, WHO SHE HAD CHOSEN TO BE HER GODFATHER, ON HER CELL PHONE ON THE WAY TO THE STUDIO TO DO HER RADIO SHOW.

FROM THE MOMENT THE DOCTOR GAVE HER THE GRIM DIAGNOSIS, SHE KNEW ONE OF GREATEST FEARS HAD BECOME A REALITY.

IT WAS FOUR DAYS AFTER HER SECOND OPERATION AND HER ENTIRE RIGHT BREAST WAS SWOLLEN AND HER ARMPIT WAS SWOLLEN WITH LYMPHATIC FLUID AND SHE JUST BROKE DOWN.

LAURA IMMEDIATELY UNDERSTOOD WHY PAT HAD BEEN ONE OF THE TOP LITIGATORS IN WASHINGTON LEGAL CIRCLES - HE HAD A HECK OF A CLOSING ARGUMENT.

PAT'S PEP TALK WAS EXACTLY WHAT LAURA NEEDED TO GET TO THE STUDIO.

DURING COMMERCIAL BREAKS, SHE SAID LITTLE PRAYERS TO HELP HER MAKE IT THROUGH.

WHEN THE CLOSING THEME MUSIC PLAYED ON HER SHOW THAT DAY, LAURA WAS GRATEFUL SHE HAD THE STRENGTH TO DRAW ON TO KEEP HERSELF TOGETHER.

SHE PRAYED FOR THOSE NOT AS LUCKY AS HER, THE PEOPLE ACROSS THE COUNTRY IN HOSPITALS AND NURSING HOMES WHO FELT FRIGHTENED AND ALONE.

DURING THE SAME TIME PERIOD LAURA WAS BEING BLESSED WITH GOOD FORTUNE REGARDING HER HEALTH, HER TALK-RADIO CAREER WAS TAKING OFF LIKE A ROCKET.

LAURA LAUNCHED "THE LAURA INGRAHAM SHOW" IN APRIL, 2001 AND IT IS NOW HEARD ON 306 STATIONS AND ON XM SATELLITE RADIO.

LAURA ALSO HAS HAD TO CONTINUALLY RESPOND TO THOSE WHO ACCUSE HER OF BEING A BIGOT DUE TO BOTH HER CATHOLIC BELIEFS AND HER PAST STATEMENTS.

THE GREATEST CONTROVERSY OF LAURA'S CAREER CAME NOT WHILE SHE WAS DISCUSSING ABORTION, ILLEGAL IMMIGRATION, HOMOSEXUALITY OR ANY OTHER HOT-BUTTON AMERICAN SOCIAL ISSUE, BUT FROM COMMENTS SHE MADE ABOUT THE IRAQ WAR.

IN MARCH OF 2006, INGRAHAM WENT ON A SIX-DAY TOUR OF IRAQ, VISITING HOSPITALS, ORPHANAGES AND IRAQI VILLAGES. UPON RETURNING TO THE UNITED STATES, SHE APPEARED ON NBC'S "TODAY SHOW" TO CRITICIZE THE MAINSTREAM AMERICAN MEDIA FOR ITS UNWILLINGNESS TO REPORT "THE TRUTH" OF THE IRAQ SITUATION. SHE SAID THAT NBC HAD FOCUSED ON PROGRAMMING "WHERE IN THE WORLD IS MATT LAUER?" AND THAT "TO DO A SHOW FROM IRAQ MEANS TO TALK TO THE IRAQI MILITARY, TO GO OUT WITH THE IRAQI MILITARY, TO ACTUALLY HAVE A CONVERSATION WITH THE PEOPLE INSTEAD OF REPORTING FROM HOTEL BALCONIES ABOUT THE LATEST IEDS GOING OFF."

WASHINGTON POST WRITER JONATHAN FINER LATER REPORTED THAT LAURA "RARELY, IF EVER, SPENT A MOMENT OUTSIDE THE PROTECTION OF U.S. FORCES OR A NIGHT OUTSIDE A MILITARY BASE." FINER COMPARED HER EXPERIENCE WITH THAT OF THE IRAQ-STATIONED JOURNALISTS SHE CRITICIZED, "ALMOST ALL OF WHOM OPERATE WITHOUT MILITARY PROTECTION." , WHILE THE NATIONAL REVIEW'S TIM GRAHAM APPLAUDED LAURA FOR BRINGING OUT THE "FACTS THE MEDIA SELF-DEFENSE TEAMS IGNORE,"

LAURA SPOKE – AND CONTINUES TO SPEAK – SO PASSIONATELY ABOUT THE IRAQ WAR BECAUSE SHE CONSIDERS THE AMERICANS WHO HAVE VOLUNTEERED TO SERVE THEIR COUNTRY AS TRUE HEROES, BECAUSE IN HER WORDS "THEY FIGHT NOT ONLY FOR THEMSELVES BUT FOR ALL OF US.

IN THE SPRING OF 2005, SHE MET ONE OF THESE YOUNG HEROES AT WALTER REED MEDICAL CENTER – 19-YEAR-OLD MARINE CORPORAL KADE HINKHOUSE.

CPL. HINKHOUSE'S HUMVEE HAD BEEN HIT MONTHS EARLIER BY AN IED, LEAVING A GAPING HOLE IN THE RIGHT SIDE OF HIS SKULL, TAKING HIS RIGHT LEG, AND PARALYZING THE LEFT SIDE OF HIS BODY. HIS BRAIN INJURY LEFT HIS SPEECH IMPAIRED BUT, IN LAURA'S OPINION, HE STILL MANAGED TO CONVEY MORE WISDOM ABOUT THE SITUATION IN IRAQ THAN MOST PEOPLE SHE HAD INTERVIEWED ON CAPITOL HILL.

A YEAR LATER, CPL. HINKHOUSE STOPPED BY LAURA'S STUDIO AFTER 18 MONTHS IN RECOVERY. HE WAS ON HIS WAY HOME TO COLORADO – HIS HAIR HAD GROWN BACK, HE WAS FITTED WITH A HIGH-TECH PROSTHESIS, AND HE HAD REGAINED MUCH OF THE MOVEMENT IN HIS LEFT ARM.

LAURA WAS OVERJOYED TO SEE HIM AND HIS VASTLY IMPROVED CONDITION.

SHE FEELS IT IS VITALLY IMPORTANT THAT EVERYONE, NOT JUST THE MILITARY, PRACTICES "SACRIFICIAL CONCERN" IN THEIR DAILY LIVES. SHE EXPERIENCED THIS FIRSTHAND MANY TIMES DURING HER CANCER BATTLE.

THE FIRST TIME WAS WHEN SHE DROVE OUT TO A PICNIC AT HER FRIEND ANN'S HOUSE AND RAN INTO DAN AND SANDY CASEY, A COUPLE SHE ONLY KNEW CASUALLY.

SANDY EVEN GAVE LAURA HER BUSINESS CARD WITH A FUNNY, UPLIFTING NOTE ON THE BACK OF IT.

Welcome to your new

IT TURNED OUT LAURA DIDN'T NEED TO TAKE DAN AND SANDY UP ON THEIR KIND INVITATION BECAUSE A FRIEND FROM HER LAW FIRM DAYS NAMED KATIE OFFERED TO MOVE INTO LAURA'S HOUSE DURING THE TOUGHEST MONTHS OF HER CHEMOTHERAPY.

LAURA WOULD HEAR FROM OTHER OLD FRIENDS AS WELL DURING HER TIME OF NEED.

THOUGH LAURA RESIDES IN WASHINGTON, D.C. AND FELICIA LIVED IN NEW YORK AND HADN'T SEEN LAURA IN FIVE YEARS, SHE WAS ON HER DOORSTEP THE NEXT DAY WITH A BAG OF GIFTS AND A BIG SMILE.

LAURA'S GREATEST MOMENT OF JOY DURING THIS TRYING PERIOD WAS WHEN HER FRIENDS PAT AND BECKY, A FEW WEEKS INTO HER ILLNESS, ASKED HER TO BE THE GODMOTHER TO THEIR DAUGHTER SOFIA, WHO WAS DUE IN THE EARLY SUMMER AND WOUND UP MIRACULOUSLY BEING BORN ON THE DAY LAURA STARTED CHEMOTHERAPY.

LAURA'S BROTHERS AND FRIENDS TOOK TURNS JOINING HER DURING HER FOUR THREE-HOUR SESSIONS IN THE CHEMO ROOM.

HER PAL PATTY JOKED ABOUT SNEAKING IN MARGARITAS.

TO LAURA, THEY WERE REAL-LIFE ANGELS AND SHE WAS EXTREMELY GRATEFUL TO HAVE THEM.

LAURA WOULD EVENTUALLY MAKE A FULL RECOVERY AND NOW CAN REGULARLY BE SEEN DEBATING ISSUES PASSIONATELY WHETHER IT'S POLITICAL FRIENDS LIKE BILL O'REILLY...

...AND POLITICAL OPPONENTS LIKE WHOOPI GOLDBERG AND JOY BEHAR.

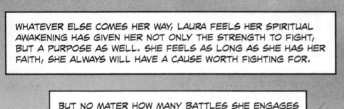

WHATEVER ELSE COMES HER WAY, LAURA FEELS HER SPIRITUAL AWAKENING HAS GIVEN HER NOT ONLY THE STRENGTH TO FIGHT, BUT A PURPOSE AS WELL. SHE FEELS AS LONG AS SHE HAS HER FAITH, SHE ALWAYS WILL HAVE A CAUSE WORTH FIGHTING FOR.

BUT NO MATER HOW MANY BATTLES SHE ENGAGES IN, SHE SAYS THE MOST IMPORTANT THING IS THAT SHE FEELS INNER PEACE.

I'VE GOTTEN TO A SPECIAL PLACE. I NEVER USED TO FEAR DYING, BUT I THINK I WAS KIND OF WORRIED ABOUT IT. BUT NOW, I'M NOT SO WORRIED ABOUT IT ANYMORE. BECAUSE I'VE EXPERIENCED AN AWAKENING.

BECAUSE IT'S NOT ENOUGH FOR US TO DEFEND AMERICAN SOIL OR TO MAINTAIN A THRIVING ECONOMY. IT WILL ALL BE IN VAIN IF WE FAIL TO NURTURE AND REFRESH AMERICA'S SOUL. AND THAT IS ONLY POSSIBLE THROUGH INDIVIDUAL BELIEF DEMONSTRATED THROUGH ACTION.

IF WE WISH TO BE A MORAL PEOPLE DEDICATED TO PRESERVING LIBERTY AND TRUE FREEDOM, THEN WE MUST FIND A WAY TO AVOID THE TEMPTING SNARES LITTERING THE CULTURAL LANDSCAPE. THIS DEMANDS THE SAME RESOLVE GEORGE WASHINGTON'S MEN HAD AT THE FOUNDING OF THE REPUBLIC. THE STAKES ARE JUST AS HIGH.

THE COMMONSENSE IDEAS AND CREATIVE STRATEGIES I SPOUT DAILY ARE INDISPENSABLE FOR OUR GROWTH AS A PEOPLE AND A NATION. YET WITHOUT FAITH TO SUSTAIN US THROUGH GOOD TIMES AND BAD., WITHOUT OUR BELIEF IN THE ALMIGHTY TO RENEW OUR SENSE OF PURPOSE, ALL OUR EFFORTS WILL BE STILLBORN. THE CULTURE, POLITICS, THE MEDIA, EVERYTHING AROUND US IS A REFLECTION OF NOT JUST OUR NATIONAL SOUL – BUT OUR INDIVIDUAL SOULS AS WELL. EACH MORAL CHOICE WE MAKE REVERBERATES INTO THE LIVES OF THOSE AROUND US AND THROUGHOUT THE WORLD

WHETHER THE NEXT GENERATION WILL ENJOY THOSE GOD-GIVEN RIGHTS OF LIFE, LIBERTY AND THE PURSUIT OF HAPPINESS HINGES ON OUR CHOICES – THE PERSONAL MORAL CHOICES WE MAKE TODAY AND THROUGHOUT OUR LIVES. ONLY BY BEING ROOTED IN FAITH AND FOLLOWING OUR INDIVIDU-AL CONSCIENCES WILL WE HAVE THE CLARITY TO RECOGNIZE WHAT IS TRUE IN ORDER TO RESIST THE FALSE PROMISES OF THE IN-CROWD. ONLY THEN CAN WE SUMMON THE MORAL RESOLVE NECESSARY TO RESCUE OUR CULTURE, OUR COUNTRY AND FUTURE GENERATIONS.

THIS IS TRUE POWER. THIS IS ETERNAL POWER AVAILABLE TO ALL OF US – RICH AND POOR, DEMO-CRAT AND REPUBLICAN, BLACK, WHITE, YELLOW, AND BROWN. IT IS THE POWER THAT NO INDIVIDUAL, INSTITUTION, OR OUTSIDE FORCE CAN TAKE AWAY FROM US.

AFTER ALL, GOD ALMIGHTY IS THE ULTIMATE SUPER POWER.

M.DÍAZ

TIDALWAVE COMICS

Writer: John Blundell
Art: Todd Tenant

Ayn Rand

Writer: CW Cooke
Art: Luciano Kars

Michele Bachmann

Writer: Michael Troy
Pencils: Manuel Díaz

Nancy Reagan

Writer: Jerome Maida
Art: Manuel Díaz

Laura Ingraham

Cover

Jaume Font

Darren G. Davis
Publisher

Susan Ferris
Entertainment Manager

TIDALWAVE PRODUCTIONS